Copyright © 2020 Clifton Townes
All rights reserved.
ISBN: 9798627992815

DEDICATION

All rights reserved. Neither this book nor any portion thereof may be reproduced or used in any manner whatsoever without the express written permission.

Disclaimer: The following book is for entertainment and informational purposes only. The information presented is without contract or any type of guarantee assurance. While every caution has been taken to provide accurate and current information, it is solely the reader's responsibility to check all information contained in this article before relying upon it. Neither the author nor publisher can be held accountable for any errors or omissions. Under no circumstances will any legal responsibility or blame be held against the author or publisher for any reparation, damages, or monetary loss due to the information presented, either directly or indirectly. This book is not intended as legal or medical advice. If any such specialized advice is needed, seek a qualified individual for help.

Trademarks are used without permission. Use of the trademark is not authorized by, associated with, or sponsored by the trademark owners. All trademarks and brands used within this book are used with no intent to infringe on the trademark owners and only used for clarifying purposes.

We hope you enjoy the Winnipeg Jets Trivia Quiz Book.

CONTENTS

QUIZ 1 4

QUIZ 2 6

QUIZ 3 8

QUIZ 4 10

QUIZ 5 12

QUIZ 6 14

QUIZ 7 16

QUIZ 8 18

QUIZ 9 20

QUIZ 10 22

QUIZ 11 24

QUIZ 12 26

QUIZ 13 28

QUIZ 14 30

QUIZ 1

1. The 2017 NHL Entry Draft was held in Chicago, IL, and the Winnipeg Jets' first pick came at number 24 overall. Which Finnish youngster did they choose?
2. At the 2016 NHL Entry Draft in Buffalo, NY, the Winnipeg Jets were sitting pretty with the number two overall pick (thanks to some luck in the draft lottery). They chose 18-year-old Patrik Laine... from what country?
3. At the 2015 NHL Entry Draft, the Winnipeg Jets had their first round pick at #17. Which other team's (a divisional rival) first round pick did they get to use?
4. Following the conclusion of the 2013-14 NHL season, the Winnipeg Jets began their workup to the 2014-15 season with the 2014 NHL Entry Draft. A Dane from the Halifax Mooseheads, who was the Jets' first pick, at ninth overall?
5. It took two full seasons for the NHL Board of Governors to finally settle on a realignment that accounted for the Atlanta Thrashers becoming the Winnipeg Jets. Six divisions became four. In which division did the Jets find themselves?
6. Before the NHL lockout began in the fall, the Winnipeg Jets locked up a few long-term contracts with their players. Which one of these did *not* sign a new contract or extension in the 2012 off-season?
7. With the franchise having just moved from another city, and with no division realignment yet, what division did the Jets play in during their first year in Winnipeg?
8. After many years of rumours and innuendo, it was finally announced on May 31st 2011 that the True North Sports and Entertainment group (TNSE) had come to an agreement on the purchase of an NHL franchise. Which team did they buy?
9. How many games did rookie goaltender Kari Lehtonen play for the Thrashers in the season?

ANSWERS QUIZ 1

1. Kristian Vesalainen
2. Finland
3. St. Louis Blues
4. Nikolaj Ehlers (LW)
5. Central Division
6. Bryan Little (C)
7. Southeast Division
8. Atlanta Thrashers
9. 4

QUIZ 2

1. Which player wore number 13?
2. Which player led the team in points?
3. Who did the Atlanta Thrashers beat for their first home win in franchise history?
4. The 2017 off season saw a number of player transactions including the acquisition and loss of a number of free agents. Which Jets goaltender accepted an offer for a one-year contract with the New York Rangers?
5. Over the summer, eleven players signed new or extended contracts with the Jets organization. Which one of them, Winnipeg's first-ever draft pick in 2011, signed an eight-year extension?
6. Seven different players signed new or renewed contracts over the summer of 2015, including one player who returned to the Jets after playing two years with Ak Bars Kazan of the Kontinental Hockey League (KHL). Who?
7. Thirteen different players signed or renewed contracts with the Jets over the summer of 2014. Which of these players, originally acquired from the Chicago Blackhawks, did NOT sign a multi-year contract?
8. The 2013 NHL Entry Draft was held in New Jersey at the end of June. With the 13th-overall selection, the Winnipeg Jets chose a defenseman from the Prince Albert Raiders of the WHL. What was his name?
9. Which Winnipeg Jet was part of the NHL Players' Association (NHLPA) Negotiating Committee that worked on establishing a new collective bargaining agreement with the NHL?

ANSWERS QUIZ 2

1. Slava Kozlov
2. Ilya Kovalchuk
3. Calgary Flames
4. Ondrej Pavelec
5. Mark Scheifele
6. Alexander Burmistrov
7. Michael Frolik (RW)
8. Josh Morrissey
9. Ron Hainsey

QUIZ 3

1. Craig Ramsey, the coach of the 2010-11 Atlanta Thrashers, did not move to Winnipeg with the rest of the team. Rather, Jets ownership named Claude Noel as the new coach of the Winnipeg Jets. Which AHL team did Noel coach before taking over the Jets?
2. Immediately following the announcement of the franchise purchase, TNSE launched a season-ticket campaign on June 1st called 'Drive-to-13,000'. The first three days of the campaign were limited to former Manitoba Moose season ticket holders, who snapped up 7,158 tickets. At noon on June 4th, 2011 the general public were able to purchase season tickets. How long did it take for 13,000 to be reached?
3. What team did Dany Heatley play his first game of the season against?
4. Number 15 had a terrific season. Who had this great season?
5. Who was the Atlanta Thrasher's coach during the 2003-04 season?
6. Which team did the Thrashers beat to get their first ever shutout?
7. Apart from dealing with the free agency market, General Manager Kevin Cheveldayoff also re-signed a number of players. Which Jets forward, drafted in 2014, signed a seven-year contract valued at $42 million?
8. After team captain Andrew Ladd was traded to Chicago the previous season, management did not immediately name a replacement. This was rectified on August 31st as the 2015-16 team points leader was named to the job. Who became the new captain?

ANSWERS QUIZ 3

1. Manitoba Moose
2. 2 minutes
3. St. Louis Blues
4. Dany Heatley
5. Bob Hartley
6. New York Islanders
7. Nikolaj Ehlers
8. Blake Wheeler

QUIZ 4

1. Early in the season, the captain of the Winnipeg Jets earned a significant milestone in his career. Who played his 700th NHL game on October 27th?
2. Jets General Manager Kevin Cheveldayoff locked up some key players to long-term (at least five-year) contracts in the 2013 offseason. Which of these was NOT one of them?
3. The Winnipeg Jets drafted defenseman Jacob Trouba in the first round (9th overall) of the 2012 NHL Entry Draft. How many games did he play in the 2012-13 season?
4. Which Jets player was the captain of the Atlanta Thrashers in the year prior to the move to Winnipeg, and continued to fill the role with the 'new' team?
5. On June 9th, 2011 TNSE announced the name of the General Manager of their new, as of yet unnamed team. Who was it?
6. Who finished second in the Thrashers' scoring race in 2004?
7. Which number did goaltender Pasi Nurminen wear?
8. How many shutouts did goaltender Pasi Nurminen record?
9. Who scored the 1st goal in franchise history?
10. At the start of the season, the Jets stumbled out of the gate, losing spectacularly in their first two games 7-2 to Toronto and 6-3 to Calgary. Fans began calling for the coach to be fired! Who was the coach for Winnipeg in the 2017-18 season?

ANSWERS QUIZ 4

1. Andrew Ladd
2. Al Montoya (G)
3. 0
4. Andrew Ladd
5. Kevin Cheveldayoff
6. Shawn McEachern
7. 31
8. 3
9. Kelly Buchberger
10. Paul Maurice

QUIZ 5

1. Four goaltenders vied for two positions on the Jets roster during preseason play. When the regular season began on October 13th, Connor Hellebuyck and Michael Hutchinson remained while Eric Comrie and Ondrej Pavelec were sent down to which AHL affiliate?

2. Injuries played a role as three different goalies shared nearly equal game time over the season. Which of these was NOT one of them?

3. Which Jet, known for his unorthodox play and capable of playing both Defense and Forward, was the only member of the team to be selected for the NHL All-Star Game?

4. Midway through the 2013-14 season, on January 12th, head coach Claude Noel was fired, finishing his year with a 19-23-5 record and a five-game losing streak. Who took over as his replacement?

5. With a shortened season, teams were limited to playing within their own conference. Which of these divisions did the Winnipeg Jets NOT play against?

6. The last NHL game played in Winnipeg before 2011 was when the original Jets were knocked out of the first round of the 1996 playoffs by the Detroit Red Wings on April 28th. Which team faced off against the Jets for their 2011 home opener (also an Original Six team)?

7. With the impending arrival of a new NHL franchise, TNSE needed to find somewhere to move their AHL team, the Manitoba Moose. To which Canadian city was the franchise moved?

8. Ilya Kovalchuk scored three goals in a game against which of the following goalies?

ANSWERS QUIZ 5

1. Manitoba Moose

2. Eric Comrie

3. Dustin Byfuglien (D)

4. Paul Maurice

5. Central Division

6. Montreal Canadiens

7. St. John's, Newfoundland

8. None of them

QUIZ 6

1. Number 9 just scored three goals in a game. Who scored the hat trick?
2. Which division did the Thrashers play in?
3. Which goalie was not taken in the expansion draft by the Thrashers?
4. The Jets recovered from their poor start, putting up a record of 29 wins, 13 losses, and 8 OT/SO losses coming into the NHL All-Star break at the end of January. Which two Winnipeg Jets players represented their team at the All-Star game?
5. Only one Winnipeg player was selected to go to the 2017 NHL All-Star Game in Los Angeles at the end of January. Which Jet was it?
6. Which Jets defenseman, who signed a five-year, $38 million contract extension on February 8th, was also the only player on the team to be named to the 2016 NHL All-Star Game?
7. Kevin Chevaldayoff, the General Manager of the Winnipeg Jets, after years of cautious trading, finally made a 'blockbuster' trade with the Buffalo Sabres on February 11th. Which of these Jets players was NOT involved in the trade?
8. Midway through the season, on January 12th, head coach Claude Noel was fired. With a new head coach, the Winnipeg Jets found a new sense of purpose. How did they fare over their next 15 games?
9. Chris Mason was the Jets' backup goalie in the 2011-12 season, but he became a free agent in the off-season and signed with the Nashville Predators. Who did the Jets sign to take his place?

ANSWERS QUIZ 6

1. Marc Savard

2. Southeast

3. Damian Rhodes

4. (F) Blake Wheeler and (G) Connor Hellebuyck

5. Patrik Laine

6. Dustin Byfuglien

7. Olli Jokinen (C)

8. 11 wins, 3 losses, 1 OT loss

9. Al Montoya

QUIZ 7

1. Who was the Thrashers' leading scoring defenseman in the season?

2. Which left winger wore number 17?

3. What was the Thrashers record during the 2003-04 season?

4. What is the name of Atlanta's mascot?

5. Young Finnish superstar Patrik Laine played his second season with the Jets in 2017-18 and turned 20 after the end of the regular season. He joined an elite company of teenage record-holders by becoming the 7th teenager to score back-to-back 30-goal seasons, the 3rd teenager to score four hat tricks, and the first in 30 years to reach 80 goals scored before his 20th birthday.

6. One player achieved the impressive feat of scoring THREE hat tricks during the season (twice against the Dallas Stars), and was the only NHL player to accomplish that in the 2016-17 season. Who managed a hat trick of hat tricks?

7. But Laine also set a record for the longest point-scoring streak by a teenager at 14 games, surpassing the previous mark set by which teenage Colorado Avalanche star, who managed a 13-game streak in the 2013-14 season?

ANSWERS QUIZ 7

1. Frantisek Kaberle

2. Ilya Kovalchuk

3. 33-37-8-4

4. Thrash

5. Nathan MacKinnon

6. Patrik Laine

7. Nathan MacKinnon

QUIZ 8

1. One player achieved the impressive feat of scoring THREE hat tricks during the season (twice against the Dallas Stars), and was the only NHL player to accomplish that in the 2016-17 season. Who managed a hat trick of hat tricks?

2. On February 25th, General Manager Kevin Cheveldayoff announced a trade that would see the Jets lose their team captain to a divisional rival. With which team was the trade made?

3. Which of the newly acquired Jets made an early impact for the team by going on a nine-game point scoring streak?

4. In an otherwise lackluster season, the Jets managed to fare quite well against one demographic of opponents - the other Canadian teams. Which was the only Canadian team, captained by Jason Spezza, that the Jets could not beat?

5. In the second half of the shortened season, the Winnipeg Jets followed up their longest losing streak with their longest winning streak - both of them the same number of games. How long were the two streaks?

6. The Jets had a poor road record in their inaugural season, but with enthusiastic fans supporting them they were much stronger at home. What was their longest home winning streak of the season?

7. The 2011 NHL Entry Draft was held in Minneapolis on June 24th and 25th, 2011 and TNSE used the venue to officially dub the team as "The Winnipeg Jets", just before announcing the franchise's first pick. Earlier that day they also announced who the new head coach of the team was. Who was it?

ANSWERS QUIZ 8

1. Patrik Laine

2. Chicago Blackhawks

3. Drew Stafford

4. Ottawa Senators

5. 5 games

6. Six games

7. Claude Noel

QUIZ 9

1. Which of these players did the Thrashers not trade at some point during the 2003-04 season?

2. If I took a picture of number 27, who did I just photograph?

3. Which player returned to the Thrasher's lineup after missing 51 games due to personal reasons?

4. Who owned the Atlanta Thrashers for their first 2 seasons?

5. He wasn't the starting goaltender for the Jets at the beginning of the season, but after their poor start, he took over top spot between the pipes. Which Jets goalie went on to have a record-breaking season and a Vezina trophy nomination?

6. Despite being eliminated from playoff contention before the end of March, the Winnipeg Jets continued to put forth a strong effort right up to the end. In fact, the team set a franchise record winning streak to finish off their season. How many games in a row did they win?

7. With their captain traded away, who was immediately named as the new captain of the Winnipeg Jets?

8. Which player, Captain of the Winnipeg Jets (and Atlanta Thrashers) since 2010, led the team in 2014-15 with 24 goals and 38 assists for 62 points?

9. Which Jets goaltender, who came to the franchise from the NY Islanders, had the most shutouts for the team in the 2013-14 season?

10. The Jets did not top any statistical categories in the league in the 2012-13 season, but they did finish 30th overall in one statistic. Which one?

ANSWERS QUIZ 9

1. Francis Lessard

2. Patrick Stefan

3. Dany Heatley

4. Ted Turner

5. Connor Hellebuyck

6. 7

7. Nobody

8. Andrew Ladd (LW)

9. Al Montoya

10. Power play percentage

QUIZ 10

1. Which of these goalies played the bulk of the 2011-12 season (playing in 68 of 82 games)?

2. Once all the crazed reaction to the naming of the new Winnipeg Jets had died down, the choice for the Jets' first draft pick in 15 years was made: Mark Scheifele of the Barrie Colts. What was his overall rank in the draft?

3. Which of these players did the Thrashers not pick up from the waiver draft on October 3, 2003?

4. Scott Mellanby signed with which team for the 2004-05 season?

5. Which right winger tied a NHL record with three short-handed assists in the same game?

6. Which of the following is the the AHL affiliate of the Atlanta Thrashers?

7. Which player continued his pattern of being the Winnipeg Jets' top scorer every other year, finishing with a record of 23 goals and 68 assists for 91 points?

8. Patrik Laine surpassed the franchise rookie goal-scoring record, which had originally been set in the 2001-02 season with the Atlanta Thrashers. Whose record did Laine beat?

9. The Jets proved to be a very hot and cold team all season, never managing to string together more than two wins in a row until the very end of the season. They finished their 2015-16 campaign on a positive note with a streak of how many wins?

ANSWERS QUIZ 10

1. Ondrej Pavelec

2. 7th

3. Jean-Pierre Vigier

4. Thrashers

5. Shawn McEachern

6. Chicago Wolves

7. Blake Wheeler

8. Ilya Kovalchuk's

9. Four

QUIZ 11

1. For the first time as the (new) Winnipeg Jets (and only the second time in franchise history), the team made it to the playoffs! Who did the Jets face in the first round?

2. Which defenseman, who started his NHL career with the Boston Bruins, led the Winnipeg Jets in most penalty minutes in the 2013-14 season, with 101?

3. One of the Jets received a serious injury in February while the team was visiting the Carolina Hurricanes. During the morning practice, his femoral artery was accidentally severed by a teammate's skate. To whom did this happen?

4. Which young gun, drafted fourth overall by the Atlanta Thrashers in 2009, scored 30 goals for the Jets in 2011-12?

5. Amidst all the hype surrounding the new Jets team, business still needed to be done. Players needed to be signed, a new logo needed to be designed, and many other details needed to be worked out before training camp could begin in September. What key player, the captain of the team, was signed to a five-year contract, announced on July 5th, 2011?

6. Three players played at least 80 games for the Thrashers in the season. Which of these was not one of them?

7. The fans were watching number 23. Who were the fans watching?

8. Which player led the defensemen in power play points?

9. What team is the ECHL affiliate of the Thrashers?

10. The Winnipeg Jets set a number of franchise records with their 114-point season. When was the last time they broke 100 points?

ANSWERS QUIZ 11

1. Anaheim Ducks
2. Mark Stuart
3. Zach Redmond
4. Evander Kane
5. Andrew Ladd
6. Slava Kozlov
7. Ivan Majesky
8. Andy Sutton
9. Greenville Grrrowl
10. This was their first time

QUIZ 12

1. The Jets only made one trade during the 2016-17 season. Originally acquired from the Buffalo Sabres in a blockbuster eight-player swap in 2015, RW Drew Stafford was traded to which team in exchange for a conditional 2018 6th-round draft pick?

2. Which Jets forward continued his pattern of winning the team scoring title every other year, leading his teammates with a record of 26 goals and 52 assists for 78 points?

3. For the second time in franchise history the team made it to the playoffs. It had been a very long time since the last playoff game was played in Winnipeg. In fact, it was not since the Jets 1.0 lost their first-round series against the Detroit Red Wings before moving to Arizona to become the Phoenix Coyotes. In what year was this?

4. The leading scorer for 2013-14 led the Winnipeg Jets in goals (28) and tied for the lead in assists (41) for a career high of 69 points. That point total beat his team-leading 64 points from the 2011-12 season. Which player?

5. Not just the captain of the team, this player also finished the 2012-13 season as the top scorer for the Winnipeg Jets. What is his name?

6. With a record of 17 goals and 47 assists, which Jet player, originally drafted by the Phoenix Coyotes, led the team with 64 points at the end of the season?

ANSWERS QUIZ 12

1. Boston Bruins

2. Blake Wheeler

3. 1996

4. Blake Wheeler (RW)

5. Andrew Ladd

6. Blake Wheeler

QUIZ 13

1. Friday the 22nd of July, 2011 saw the release of the long-awaited logo for the new Winnipeg Jets; a stylized air force roundel with a silver jet superimposed on a red maple leaf. The first opportunity to see the new Jets logo on a jersey in competition against another team came in early September at the Young Stars Tournament in Pencticton, B.C. What was the result of the Jets' first clash, against the San Jose Sharks prospects?

2. The Thrashers won six games in overtime in the season. In how many of these games did Marc Savard score the winning OT goal?

3. Number 5 was worn by which defensemen?

4. How many points did Kip Brennan have in the 2003-04 season?

5. Who got the first ever hattrick for the Thrashers?

6. For only the third time in franchise history (and the second time as the Jets), Winnipeg made it to the postseason. Which team did they face in the first round?

7. The team's scoring title was traded back and forth between Andrew Ladd and Blake Wheeler in the first five years in Winnipeg. With 32 goals and 50 assists for 82 points, who claimed the title in season 2016-17?

8. Sadly, the Jets did not advance beyond the first round of the 2015 NHL Playoffs. By what margin in the best-of-seven match-up did they lose?

ANSWERS QUIZ 13

1. 4-0 win

2. 2

3. Tomas Kloucek

4. 0

5. Dean Sylvester

6. Minnesota Wild

7. Mark Scheifele

8. Apr-00

QUIZ 14

1. The Jets finished the 2013-14 season with a 37-35-10 record for a total of 84 points. Out of seven teams in their division, where did the Jets place?

2. For the second year in a row, the Jets finished out of the playoffs, but they still managed a winning record, and finished 9th in the Eastern Conference. In what position did they finish in their division?

3. With Winnipeg's dream come true, the Jets returned to the ice officially with their first pre-season matchup on September 20th, 2011, a pair of split-squad games against which Central Division team?

4. What was the highest jersey number that anyone on the Thrashers wore that season?

5. What is the name of the official game program for the Atlanta Thrashers?

6. The Winnipeg Jets knocked off their first round competitors in how many games?

7. The second round of the playoffs was terra incognito for the Winnipeg Jets, who had never won a series before this year. Who was their second round opponent (and President's Trophy winning team)?

ANSWERS QUIZ 14

1. 7th

2. 2nd

3. Columbus Blue Jackets

4. 49

5. The Winger Magazine

6. 5

7. Nashville Predators

Manufactured by Amazon.ca
Bolton, ON